Succeed In Reading and Writing

Jane Hartzig
illustrations by Jim H

Contents

Introduction

Published by
Arcturus Publishing Limited
for Bookmart Limited
Registered number 2372865
Trading as Bookmart Limited
Desford Road, Enderby,
Leicester LE9 5AD

This edition published 2002

ISBN 1-84193-101-2

Printed and bound in China

Author: Jane Hartzig
Illustrator: Jim Hansen
Editor: Rebecca Panayiotou
Designer: Susi Martin-Taylor
Cover designer: Alex Ingr
Series consultant: Maureen Robinson

Succeed In Reading and Writing is a beautifully illustrated and stimulating introduction to literacy for children in the early years of their formal education.

By the end of Key Stage 1, children should be able to put their ideas into sentences; use capital letters, full stops and question marks; grasp the nature and use of nouns, verbs and pronouns; recognise rhyme, alliteration and other sound patterns, and use their knowledge of sequence and story language to retell stories and predict events.

This book looks carefully at these and other main topics of the National Curriculum with the objective of improving your child's understanding, speed and accuracy in reading and writing.

How to use this book

- Don't attempt to finish the whole book in one session! Each child is an individual and will have a different concentration span. A topic a day can be taken, or more if the child has the energy.
- Help your child by reading the instructions for them and explaining what is required in the exercises. If they have difficulty with any of the tasks, you can help them.
- Each time your child has completed a page of this book, give them lots of praise and encouragement. Increase their sense of achievement by awarding them a star.

Good luck and good practising!

All about me!

This is your book. Write some things about yourself.

My name is ______________________________________.

I am ________ years old.

I live in ____.

My favourite toy is _______________________________.

Draw a line from each word to the correct part of the picture to name the different parts of your head.

Now write the correct word in each space to label the parts of your body. Use the list to help you.

arm

head

foot

hand

leg

stomach

head

Well done! Award yourself a star!

Sentences

A **sentence** is a group of words that makes sense. We all use sentences when we speak and when we write. A sentence can be a statement, a question or a command. Here are some examples:

Tommy eats breakfast every day.	(Statement)
Why are you laughing?	(Question)
Put your shoes on now.	(Command)

These sentences have been split in half! Make sense of them by drawing a line to join the beginning of each sentence to the correct ending.

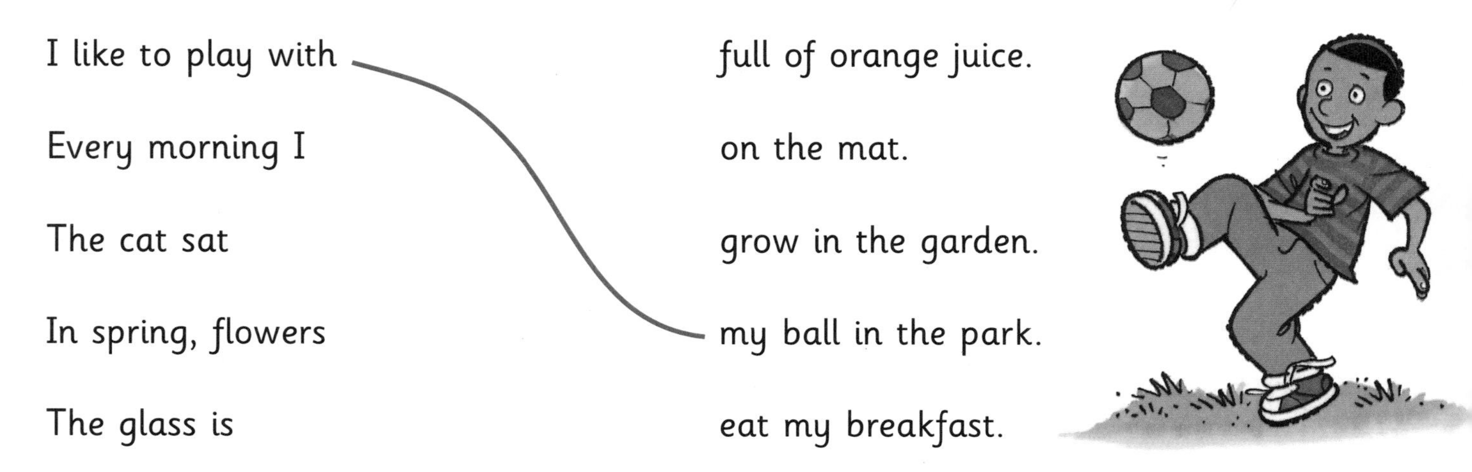

I like to play with	full of orange juice.
Every morning I	on the mat.
The cat sat	grow in the garden.
In spring, flowers	my ball in the park.
The glass is	eat my breakfast.

Here are some more muddled sentences. "cat The on sat mat the." - does not make sense, but, "The cat sat on the mat." - does make sense!

Now write the following sentences so that they make sense.

The hot sun is. ______________________.

bird fly A can. ______________________.

love skip I to. ______________________.

door Close the. ______________________.

Well done! Award yourself a star!

These sentences have a word missing.
Fill in the missing words, choosing from the list.

On Monday I will go to ___________.

My Mum bakes a chocolate ___________.

It is cold, so I put my ___________ on.

The ___________ chases the chickens.

The ___________ tastes nice.

Now look at these nursery rhymes. Fill in the missing words, choosing from the list.

Humpty Dumpty sat on a _________.

Humpty Dumpty had a great _________.

All the King's _________

And all the King's _________

Couldn't put _________ together again.

Jack and Jill went up the _________

To fetch a pail of _________.

_________ fell down and hurt his crown,

And _________ came tumbling after.

Well done! Award yourself a star!

Sentences

There are three ways to end a sentence:

1. Usually, a sentence is a simple statement and we use a full stop.
   Paul lives in England.
2. When a sentence is a question, however, it ends with a question mark.
   What is the time?
3. Finally, if a sentence is an exclamation of surprise, anger, or excitement, it ends with an exclamation mark.
   Watch out, the tree is falling down!

Colour the balloons with a full stop in yellow, the balloons with a question mark in blue, and the balloons with an exclamation mark in green.

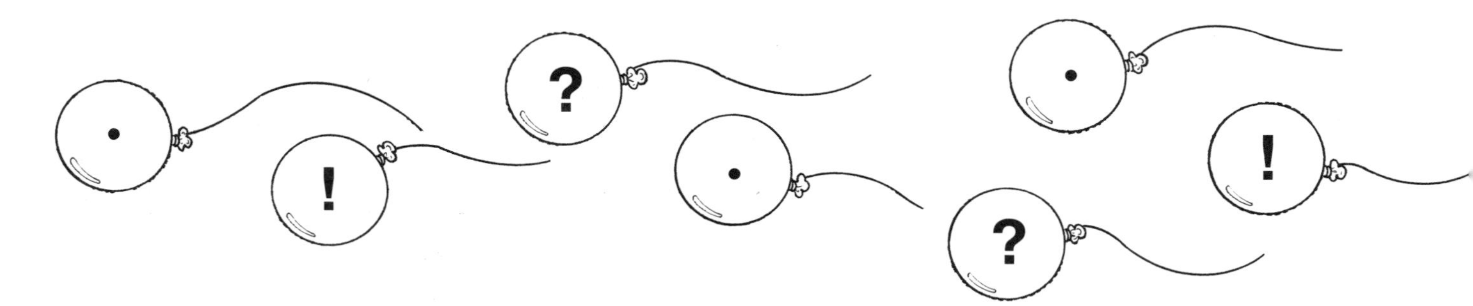

Write either a full stop, a question mark or an exclamation mark after each sentence.

What are you doing with the toy__

That is absolutely fantastic__

My mum is in the garden__

Can I have a sweet, please__

Help – the house is on fire__

My dog's name is Rover__

Well done! Award yourself a star!

A sentence always begins with a capital letter.

The sun is shining.

Where is my hat?

Leave me alone.

Something is wrong with these sentences.
Copy the sentences, and make them correct.

you are my friend. ______________________________.

the dog is brown. ______________________________.

i can skip. ______________________________.

apples are tasty. ______________________________.

Can you find the mistakes in these sentences?
Tick the box or boxes when you see the mistake.

	No capital letter	No full stop
the boy fell over and cried.	☐	☐
Apples grow on apple trees	☐	☐
my house has a red door	☐	☐
Crocodiles have very big teeth	☐	☐
the dog had a bone.	☐	☐

Well done! Award yourself a star!

The Mouse and the Lion

Once upon a time, there was a large lion who lived in the jungle. He had a beautiful mane and huge paws, which he used when he was hunting. He was very strong and very proud, and he considered himself to be the king of the jungle.

One day the lion was resting under the shade of a tree. Suddenly, a tiny mouse, who was looking for berries to feed his family, accidentally ran onto the lion's giant paws. The lion picked the mouse up by his tail.

"Yum yum, a tiny snack!" said the lion. "I shall eat you up for daring to run over my paws."

"Please don't eat me!" squeaked the mouse, who was very scared. "I was looking for food for my family! I am hardly a mouthful to a big lion like you, and if you spare my life, one day I may be able to save yours."

The lion roared with laughter. "A tiny mouse like *you* help the king of the jungle? But, as you have made me laugh, I agree. I will let you go." The lion put the mouse down, so he could go on his way.

One day, some time later, the little mouse heard a terrible roaring deep in the jungle. He thought it sounded like his friend, and he scampered off to look. He found the lion trapped in thick ropes. Hunters had set a trap, and now the lion was caught.

The mouse said, "You once spared my life, and now I can help you." The little mouse started to nibble his way through the ropes and, although it took a long time, he finally managed to free the lion.

"Thank you so much," said the lion. "I can see now how lucky I am to have you as a friend!"

Reading Comprehension

Ask an adult to read the story with you. Then talk about the story and answer the questions below.

Questions

Where did the lion live?
What was the mouse doing when it ran onto the lion's paws?
Why did the lion let the mouse go?
Who had trapped the lion?
Why did the mouse help the lion?
What do you do to help your friends?

Draw a picture of one of your friends.
Write about what you like about your friends.

Well done! Award yourself a star!

Verbs

A **verb** is the action word in a sentence.
"I play every day." The verb or action word in that sentence is **play**.
A sentence needs a verb. In a sentence, a verb can tell us:

How we move	e.g.	run, walk, tiptoe
How we talk	e.g.	whisper, shout, giggle
How we feel	e.g.	love, hate, like

There are thousands of actions we take part in, feel or talk about every day!

Look at these actions. Follow the lines to find the verb.

jump shout fish read paint

Find the verbs in the following sentences. Put a circle around the verb, and then write it out in the space provided.

Lucas goes to the birthday party. ________

I jump over the fence. ________

Rosie sings in the choir. ________

Raj bakes a chocolate cake. ________

Well done! Award yourself a star!

Here are some mixed-up socks. Colour the matching pairs in the same colours. The words are all verbs.

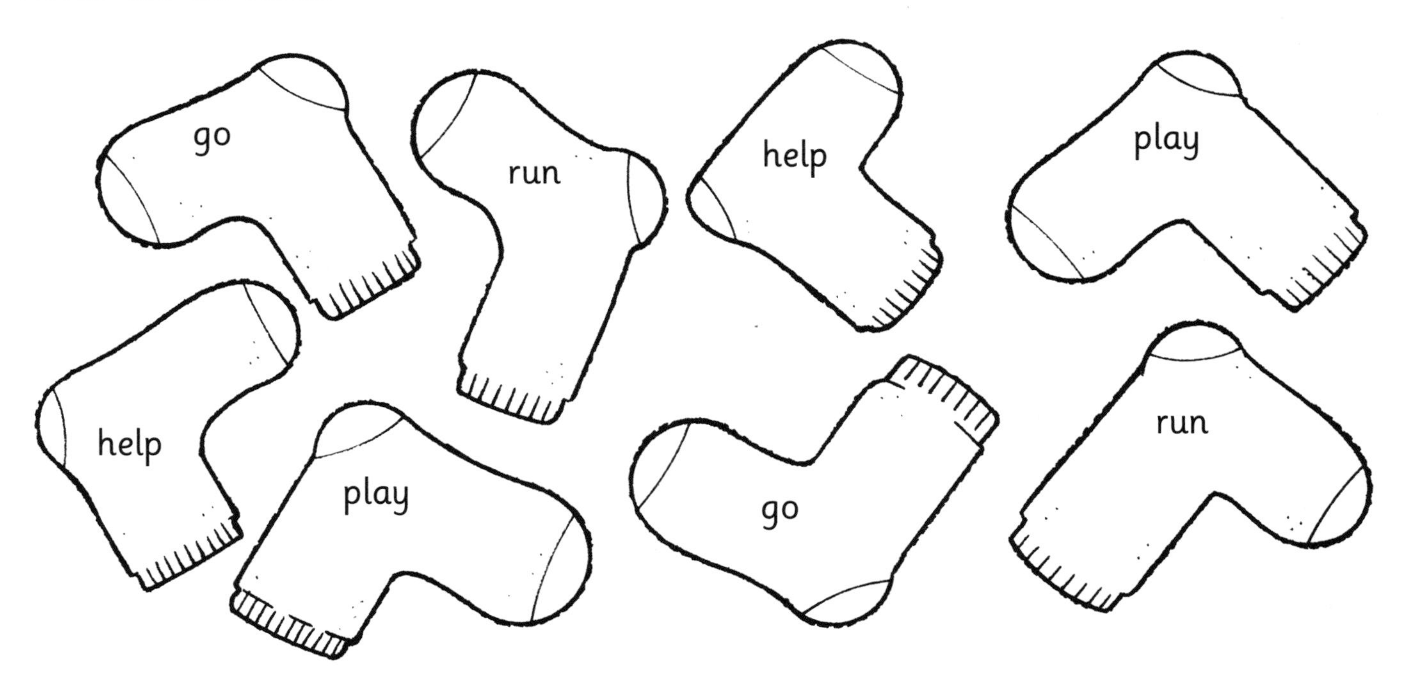

Here are some fish in the pond. Fish out the correct verbs to finish the sentences.

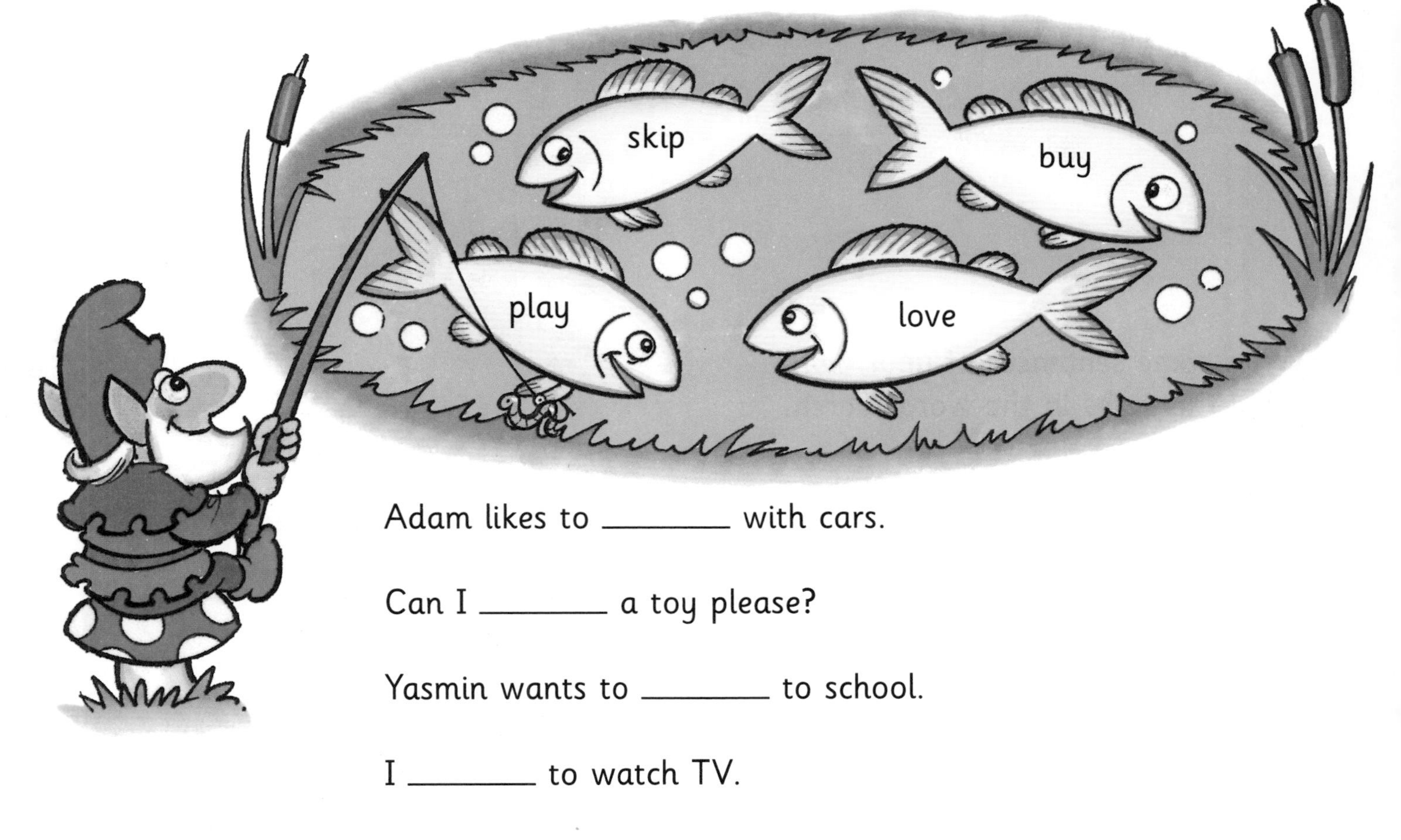

Adam likes to ________ with cars.

Can I ________ a toy please?

Yasmin wants to ________ to school.

I ________ to watch TV.

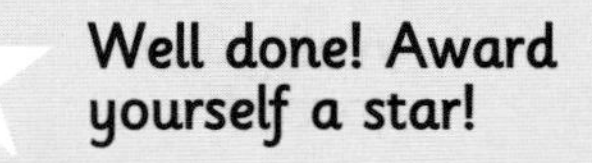

Verbs

Verb Word Search

These ten verbs are hidden in the square. Can you find them all? They can be written forwards, downwards or diagonally.

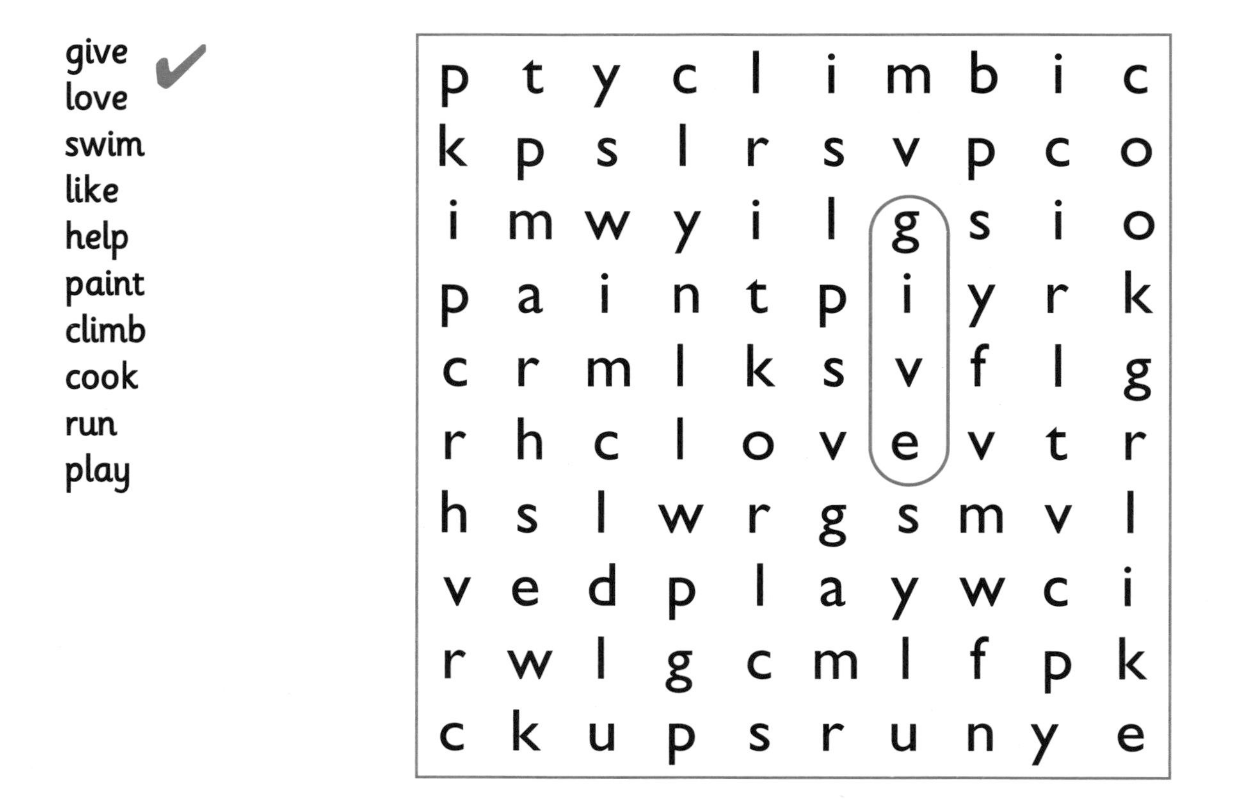

Write some sentences of your own using the verbs in the word search.

Here is a sentence to help get you started.

I climb trees.

Well done! Award yourself a star!

We can do it!

Verbs are action words. Think about the actions of these animals. Write down the action, using the list to help you.

A bird can ________________.

A fish can ________________.

A mole can ________________.

A kangaroo can ____________.

A dog can ________________.

Now think of all the actions that you can do! Write them down. Here is an action to start you off.

I can smile ______________.

I can ________________.

I can ________________.

I can ________________.

I can ________________.

I would like to ________________.

Well done! Award yourself a star!

Nouns

A noun tells us what someone or something is called. A noun can be the name of a person, an animal, a place, or a thing.

Common nouns are nouns that name people and things in general - here are some examples:

girl dog park house air computer

Circle the noun in the following sentences. Then write it out in the space provided. Use the pictures as clues!

I have my own cup. ________

My car is red. ________

She wrote a big book. ________

The bird is flying. ________

Complete the story by filling in the missing words in the same order that they appear on the path. All the words are nouns.

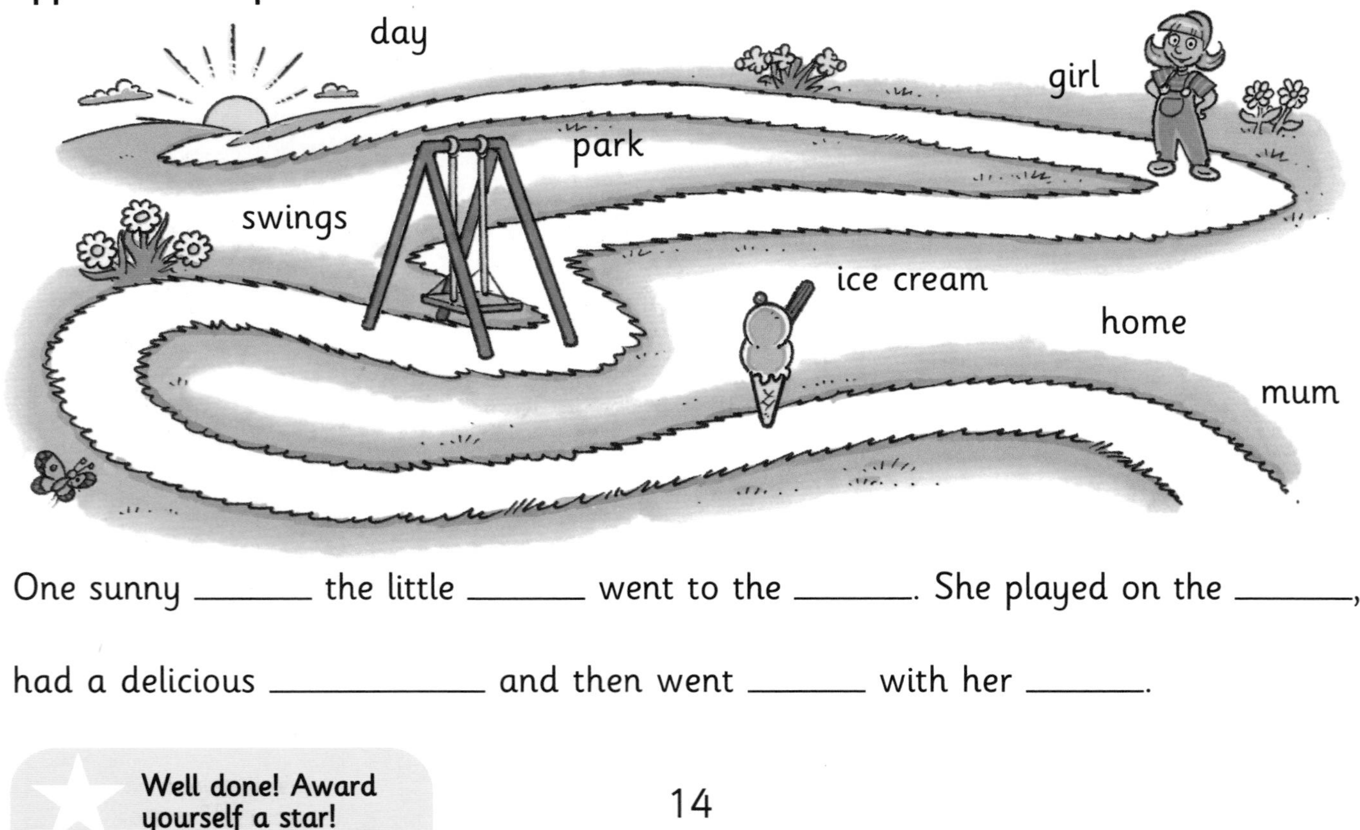

One sunny ______ the little ______ went to the ______. She played on the ______, had a delicious ___________ and then went ______ with her ______.

Well done! Award yourself a star!

Proper nouns are nouns that name a particular or special person, place or thing. Your name is a proper noun.

Proper nouns always start with a capital letter. Here are some examples:

Emily Friday April London

Names are proper nouns and always start with a capital letter.
Copy the names of the children and their pets onto the signs, starting each name with a capital letter.

Complete the sentences using the proper nouns in the brick wall.

Adam

January

Friday

Paris

____________ is a very beautiful city.

The weather is cold in ____________.

His name is ____________.

____________ is my favourite day of the week.

Well done! Award yourself a star!

Nouns

Collective nouns are nouns that name a **group** of things, people or animals. For example, a **flock** of sheep or a **swarm** of bees.

Here are some groups of animals! Write the name of the animals that the collective nouns describe.

A flock of ________ A herd of ________

A shoal of ________ A gaggle of ________

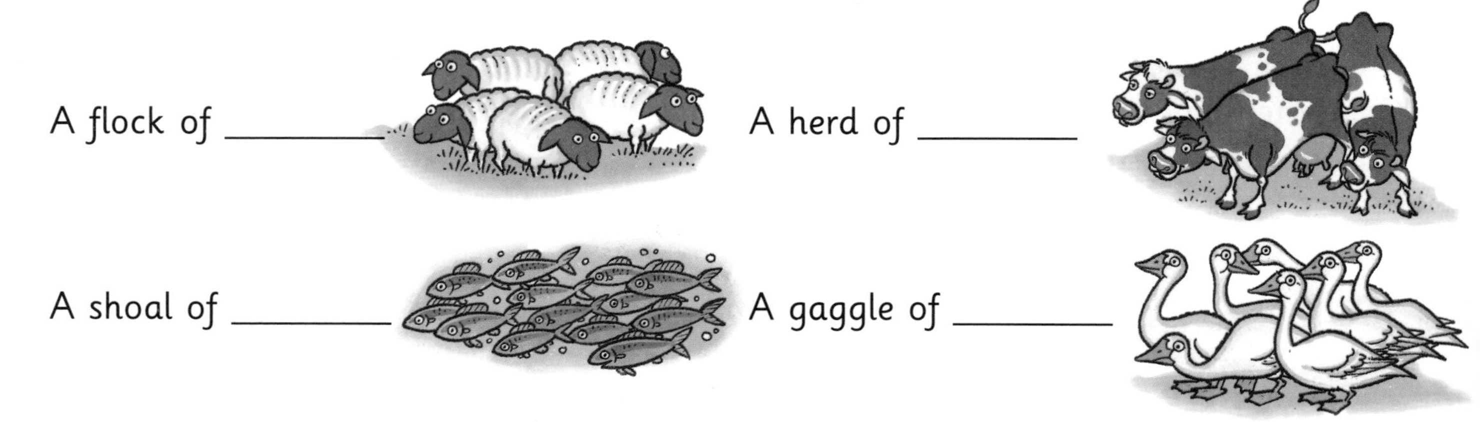

Here are some more collective nouns. Write the names of the things that they describe. The pictures will give you a clue!

A pack of ________

A forest of ________

A library of ________

A fleet of ________

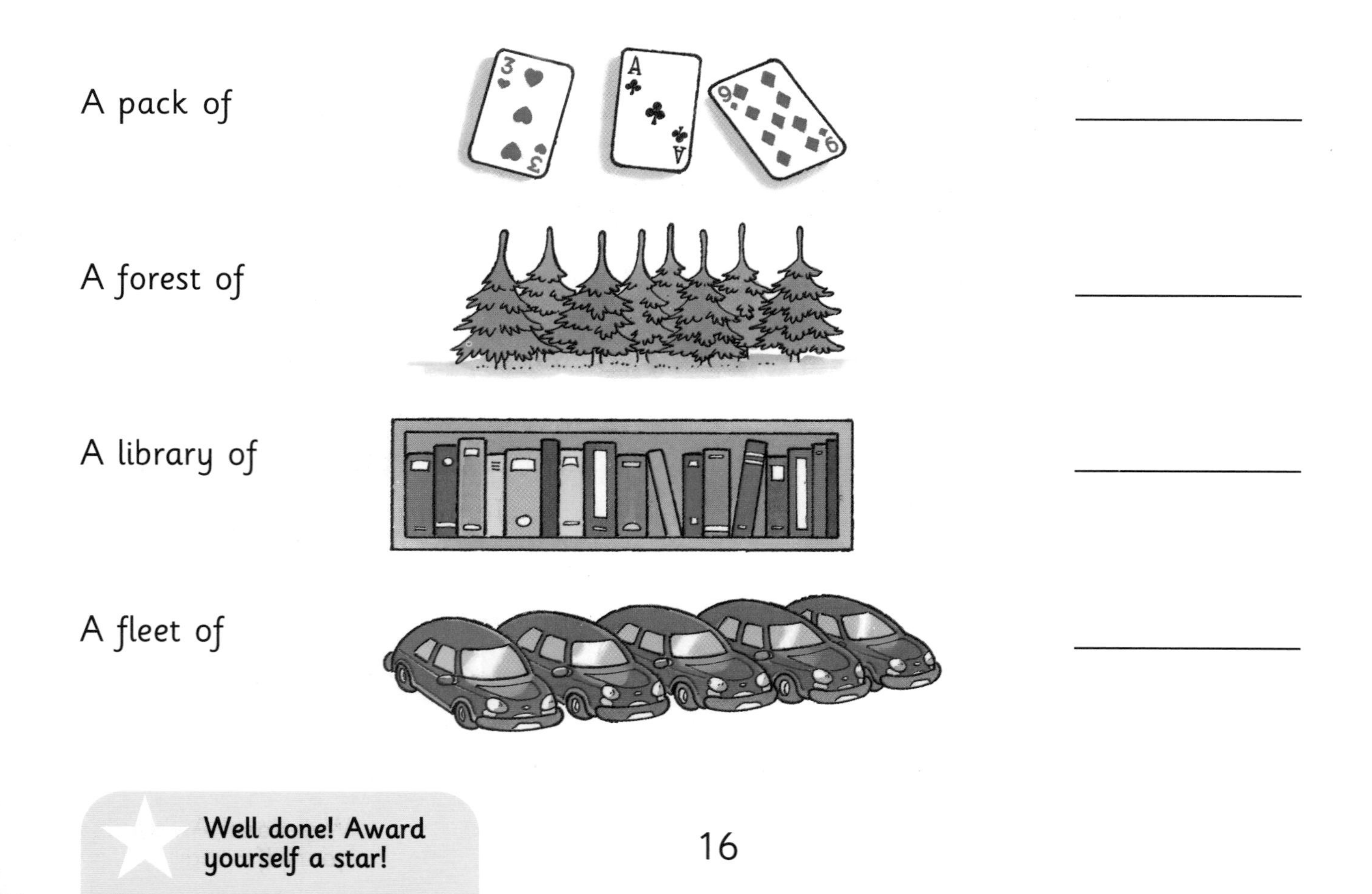

Well done! Award yourself a star!

Groups and Sets

A **group** or a **set** is a number of things that are **linked** in some way – they go together. For example, we can talk of a **group** of friends or a **set** of plates.

We can put lots of things into groups or sets. Can you group these things together?

Put a red circle around the things you can eat and a blue circle around the things you can't eat.

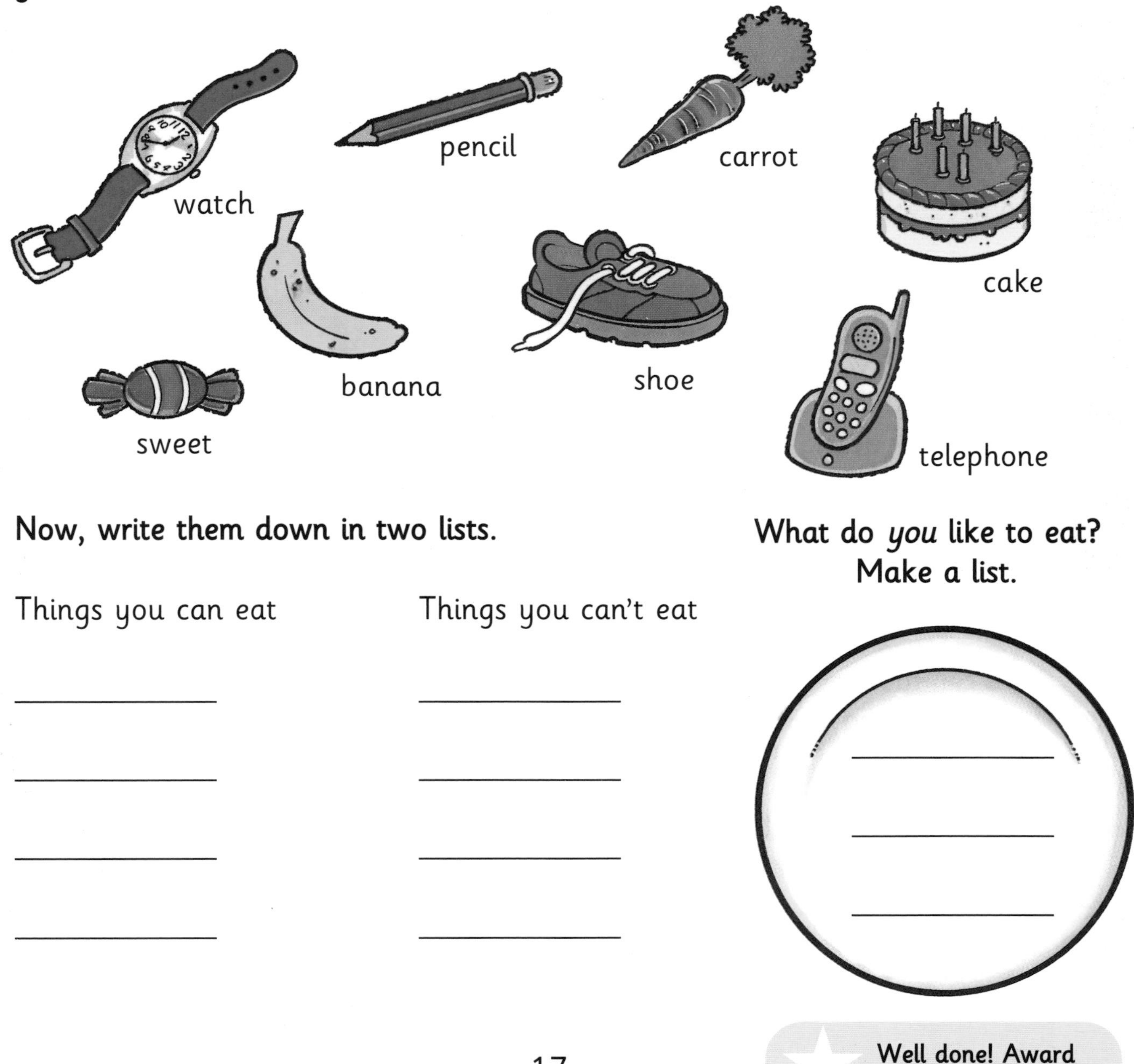

Now, write them down in two lists.

Things you can eat	Things you can't eat
____________	____________
____________	____________
____________	____________
____________	____________

What do *you* like to eat? Make a list.

____

____

____

Well done! Award yourself a star!

Lucas and the Alien

One night, Lucas was looking out of his bedroom window at the night sky. He was bored, and he couldn't sleep. There was only his sister at home today, and Lucas didn't like to play with girls. He only played with boys.

If only he had a friend to talk to! Then, suddenly, he had an idea - he would go to Mars! He had always wondered what it would be like on a different planet.

When he got there the ground was rocky and bare, and there were big boulders and huge craters everywhere. He started to look around, and very soon he saw in the distance a small alien!

"Wow!" thought Lucas. "Doesn't he look strange - I'd better not talk to him." But the alien came over to Lucas. The alien had three eyes, four noses and lots of ears sticking out of its head instead of hair - and it was red all over! Lucas hid behind a rock, but the alien followed him.

"Hello!" said a small, high voice. "My name is Fnu-Fnu. What's yours?"

"Er, Lucas," said Lucas, amazed. The alien could talk!

"Do you like my toy?" said Fnu-Fnu, and held out a big bouncy ball that glowed silvery-purple.

"I've got one of those!" said Lucas, and he pulled his green, glittery, bouncy ball from his pyjama pocket.

Lucas and Fnu-Fnu played bounce and catch until it was time for Lucas to go home.

"I have to get back for breakfast," explained Lucas. "But I've had a great time. I am so pleased to have a boy from Mars as a friend. Shall we meet again?"

"I'm not a boy, I'm a girl!" said Fnu-Fnu, laughing. "Of course we can meet again."

And from that time, whenever Lucas was bored he went to Mars to play with his friend, who happened to be a girl.

Reading Comprehension

Read the story with an adult. Then answer the questions.
Hope you enjoy it!

Questions

What was Lucas looking at out of his bedroom window?
Where did Lucas go?
What colour was Fnu-Fnu's bouncy ball?
Do you think Lucas will stay friends with Fnu-Fnu?
Why do you think it doesn't matter what your friends look like?
Draw an alien that you would make friends with, and then write all about him or her.

Well done! Award yourself a star!

Poetry Time

Sometimes, to make a story or a poem effective, a writer uses lots of words together which begin with the same letter or sound. This is called alliteration.

Read these poems with someone. What do you notice about the language?

Buzz Buzz Buzz

Buzz, buzz, buzz
Goes Billy, the honeybee.
Buzz at breakfast, brunch and tea.
Buzz all day Billy
But don't buzz me!

Frank the Forgetful Frog

Frank the funny, forgetful frog
Forgets his name most frequently.
He asks his friends, "What am I called,
Fred or Freddie, Finlay, Flora,
Florence, Francis, or is it Fedora?"
His froggie friends find Frank quite funny.
"We cannot play a naughty prank,
we will be frank," they say,
"IT'S FRANK!"

Well done! Award yourself a star!

Can you use alliteration to describe an animal? Here are a couple of examples:

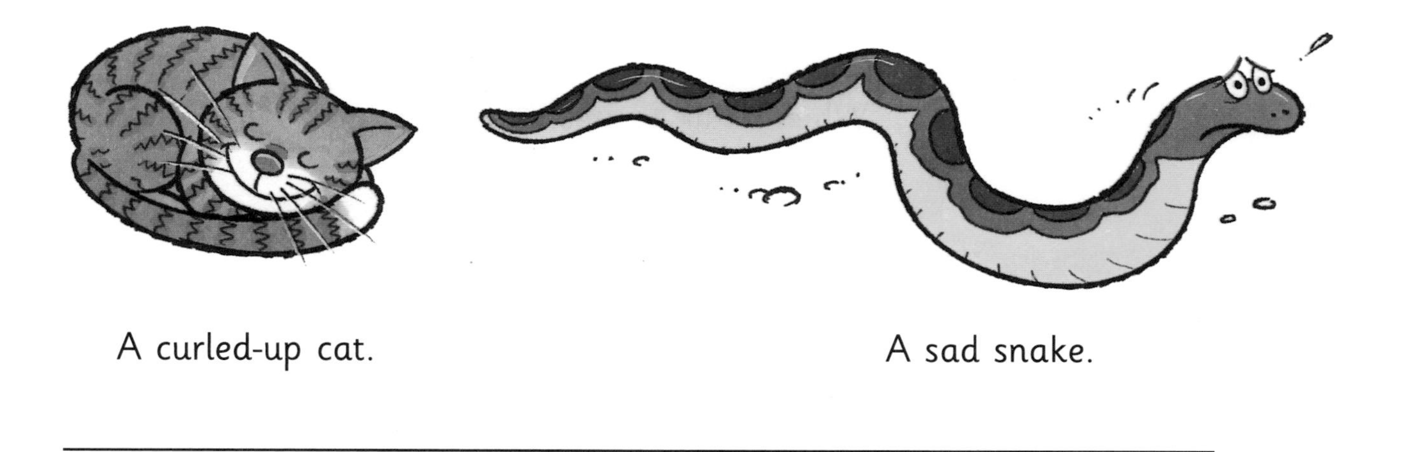

A curled-up cat.

A sad snake.

Write a sentence, or a poem. Try to make the important words start with the same letter or sound!

Here are a couple of examples to help you.

Mabel the miniature mouse munched too many mangoes.

My Dad dropped the dishes.
What a dreadful disaster!

Well done! Award yourself a star!

Pronouns

Pronouns are the names we call each other, when we are not using our 'proper' names.

I talk about myself as **I**. When I talk to people I sometimes say **you**.

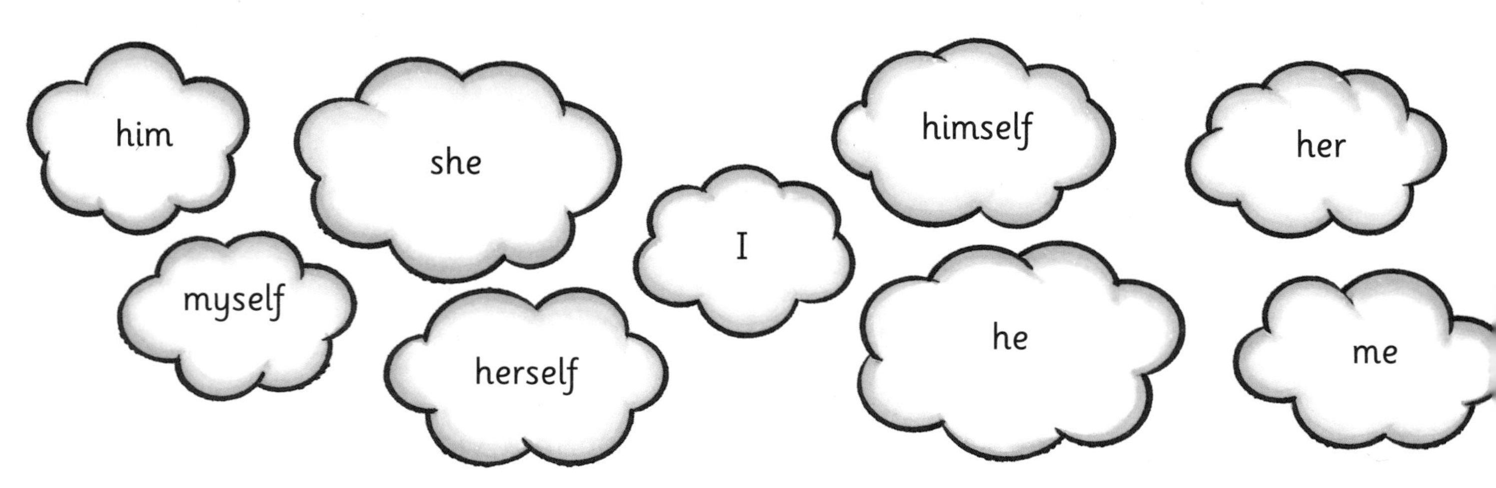

Each of these clouds contains a pronoun. Draw a picture of yourself in the space below. Now find all the words that refer to you and write them under your picture.

Now find the words that refer to a girl and to a boy and write them under the pictures.

Well done! Award yourself a star!

Pronoun Crossword

Here is a crossword. All the answers are pronouns. Fill in the missing words in the sentences to find the answers. Use the list of words to help you.

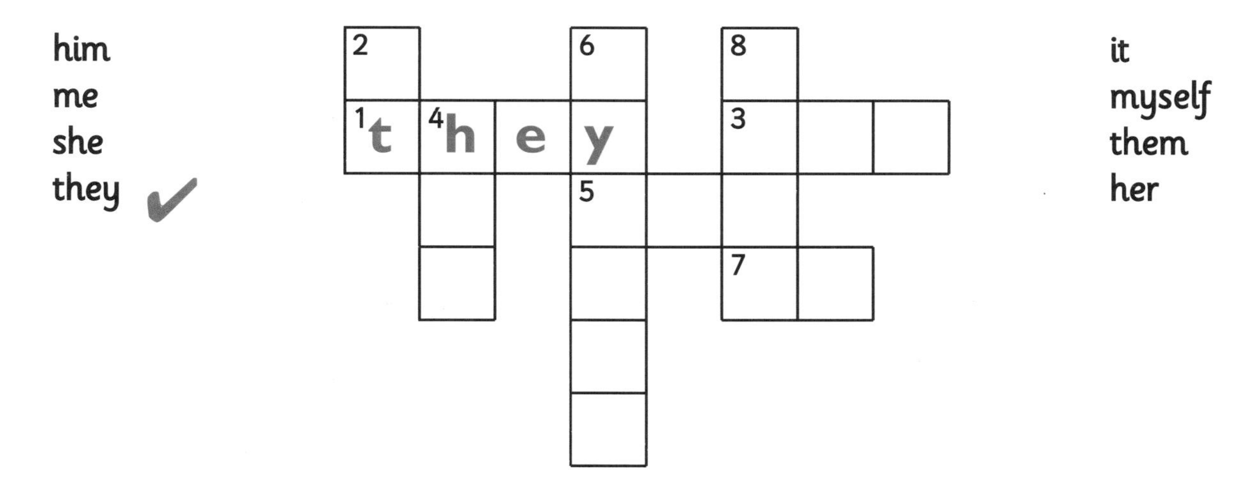

ACROSS

1. Sam and Isabel went for a walk. They walked to the park.

3. The doctor saw Tom and gave ______ some medicine.

5. Amy loved games. ______ played all day.

7. Give ______ the ball please.

DOWN

2. The chair fell over. ______ was broken.

4. Hannah loved ______ pet hamster.

6. I look at ________ in the mirror.

8. The cows were big. Daniel looked at ______.

Well done! Award yourself a star!

Creative Writing

Read the start of the story and think about what might happen next. Talk about it, and then write your own ending to the story.

Rebecca had a pet hamster, Hammy, who lived in a lovely big cage. One sunny day, Rebecca took Hammy's cage into the garden. She opened the cage, and was just about to pick Hammy up when her mother called, "Rebecca! Your friend has come to see you!" Rebecca forgot about Hammy, and went to the door. When she came back . . .

Joe was very happy. He had been given a new bike for his birthday. It even had a horn which made a loud noise! When he was blowing the candles out on his birthday cake he wished, "I wish my bike could fly!" The next day was Sunday, and Joe went for a bike ride. He turned a corner, and right in front of the bike was a huge branch! Joe put his brakes on and . . .

Well done! Award yourself a star!